The Magic School Bus®
Arctic Adventure

Arnold Ralphie Keesha Phoebe Carlos Tim Wanda Dorothy Ann

Cartwheel
·B·O·O·K·S·®

SCHOLASTIC INC.
New York Toronto London Auckland Sydney
Mexico City New Delhi Hong Kong Buenos Aires

Every day,
Ms. Frizzle wears a crazy dress.
She wears crazy shoes.

Dear Parents,

Welcome to the Scholastic Reader series. We have taken over 80 years of experience with teachers, parents, and children and put it into a program that is designed to match your child's interests and skills.

Level 1—Short sentences and stories made up of words kids can sound out using their phonics skills and words that are important to remember.

Level 2—Longer sentences and stories with words kids need to know and new "big" words that they will want to know.

Level 3—From sentences to paragraphs to longer stories, these books have large "chunks" of text and are made up of a rich vocabulary.

Level 4—First chapter books with more words and fewer pictures.

It is important that children learn to read well enough to succeed in school and beyond. Here are ideas for reading this book with your child:

- Look at the book together. Encourage your child to read the title and make a prediction about the story.
- Read the book together. Encourage your child to sound out words when appropriate. When your child struggles, you can help by providing the word.
- Encourage your child to retell the story. This is a great way to check for comprehension.

Scholastic Readers are designed to support your child's efforts to learn how to read at every age and every stage. Enjoy helping your child learn to read and love to read.

—Francie Alexander
Chief Education Officer
Scholastic Education

Frizzle   Liz

Written by Gail Herman.
Illustrations by Carolyn Bracken.

Based on *The Magic School Bus* books written by Joanna Cole
and illustrated by Bruce Degen.

The author and editor would like to thank Dr. Nick Lunn
of the Canadian Wildlife Service for his advice in preparing
the manuscript.

ISBN 0-439-68401-3

17 16 15 14   10 11 12 13 14/0

Printed in the U.S.A.   40

First printing, November 2004

We get on the Magic School Bus.
It starts to spin.
When it stops,
it is the Magic School Jet!

Soon we land.
It is daytime, but it is almost dark.
Ms. Frizzle says the Arctic is
dark for much of the winter.

IT SEEMS SO LATE!

HAVE WE MISSED LUNCH?

NIGHT AND DAY
IN THE ARCTIC
by Wanda

In the Winter, the Arctic
night can last for several
months. That's because the
top part of Earth tilts away
from the sun in the winter.

ARCTIC

SUN

EARTH

WINTER DIAGRAM

In the Arctic summer, it
is always day. During
these months, Earth tilts
toward the sun so the
Arctic gets more light.

ARCTIC

SUN

EARTH

SUMMER DIAGRAM

"Lots of animals live in the Arctic," Dorothy Ann reads.

HIDE-AND-SEEK ANIMALS

Some Arctic animals turn white in winter. This makes them hard to see on the snow and ice.

WINTER SUMMER

Arctic Hare

Snowy Owl

Arctic Fox

Bit by bit,
the snow slows down.
Then it stops.

We see some walruses
and some seals.
But we do not see the Magic School Jet!

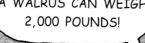

A WALRUS CAN WEIGH
2,000 POUNDS!

THAT'S A TON OF BLUBBER!

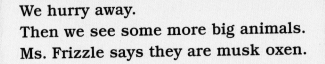

We hurry away.
Then we see some more big animals.
Ms. Frizzle says they are musk oxen.

THEY LOOK LIKE THEY ARE ALL HAIR!

A LOT OF HAIR HELPS KEEP THEM NICE AND WARM.

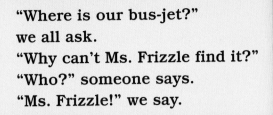

"Where is our bus-jet?"
we all ask.
"Why can't Ms. Frizzle find it?"
"Who?" someone says.
"Ms. Frizzle!" we say.

WHO SAID WHO?

LOOK, IT'S AN OWL!

Now our eyes are used to looking in the snow.
Now we can see the white owl, a white fox,
and a white hare.
They were hidden before.
They are white like the snow.

THAT HARE IS RUNNING AWAY FROM THE FOX.

OH, NO! IT'S A BAD HARE DAY.

Some of the hares jump on
a big pile of snow.
There is something under the snow.
It's the Magic School Jet!

We get in the bus-jet.
We are off!
Good-bye, Arctic!
Good-bye, Arctic animals!

I WONDER IF OUR SCHOOL WILL BE.

More about the amazing Arctic:

There is more water than land in the Arctic. The Arctic Ocean is the smallest of the four oceans. Ice covers part of the Arctic Ocean all year round. In the winter, sheets of ice can grow up to six feet thick!

KNOCK! KNOCK!
WHO'S THERE?
SNOW!
SNOW WHO?

SNOW PLACE LIKE THE ARCTIC!